GARDEN

JOURNAL

A Four-Year Record Book

Edited by Nancy K. Simpkins
Designed by Deborah Michel ❧ Illustrated by Katherine Barnwell

MICHEL PUBLISHING, LTD.
SOUTH SALEM, NEW YORK 10590

Published in the United States by
Michel Publishing Co., Ltd.
188 Kitchawan Road,
South Salem, New York 10590
(914) 533-6437

3 5 7 9 0 8 6 4

Quality printing and binding by
Inland Press
Fountain Blvd.
Menomonee Falls, WI 53051 USA

Special thanks to Marcia Leonard for her editorial help

ISBN 0-934504-86-5

ABOUT THIS BOOK

Ten years ago, my gardening style could best be described as impulsive and haphazard. If I saw a plant that appealed to me, I'd simply buy it and then find a spot to plant it. Needless to say, the results were not always harmonious. Yet it never occurred to me to draw a plan of my garden—until one year when I wanted to plant something but wasn't sure where I had room for it. There I stood, shovel in hand, too afraid to dig for fear of disturbing some slumbering plant beneath the ground.

Obviously, I couldn't continue this way. I decided that the following spring I would dig up the entire garden and start from scratch. I began making lists of plants I *had* to have, plants I *wanted* to have, and plants I thought looked well together. Then I organized them by height, blooming time, and color into a workable design. It took me all winter, but the results—my first perennial garden—were well worth the effort.

Since then I have added an old-fashioned rose garden, a rock garden, and vegetable beds. At some point I started a notebook for my designs and plant lists. Then I began jotting down other information that was pertinent to my garden: When the forsythia bloomed each year, which catalogs and suppliers had proved reliable, which variety of tomato tasted best.... I took photographs of my garden at various stages and tucked those into the notebook—along with empty seed packets and home recipes for pest control. And I recorded the lessons I had learned, so I wouldn't have to learn them again next year.

As my gardening experience grew, so did my notebook. Eventually it became too fat and unwieldy, and I bought an official gardening journal. But it seemed rigid and restrictive, and it was full of quotes and advice that were irrelevant to my garden.

What I wanted was a journal that would let me store information in an organized and accessible way and yet was flexible enough to accommodate all types of gardens. When I couldn't find such a book, I decided to create one myself—and that's what you hold in your hands. You can customize this journal for *your* type of garden and *your* part of the country. It works all year round, and it holds four years of information specific to your garden.

The first part of this book, pages 5 to 148, is an annual record divided into monthly segments. For each month you will find:

☞ **Monthly Reminders,** a place to list the chores you need to complete, such as fertilizing, pruning, mulching, or seed starting.

☞ **Week-by-Week Diary,** pages that allow you to compare notes for the same week in consecutive years—and anticipate problems before they occur.

☞ **Photographs,** album pages so you can document what your garden looks like at different times of the year.

☞ **Notes,** a page for miscellaneous comments and reminders.

The second part of the journal is for general record keeping and planning. It includes:

☞ **Plant Inventory** (pages 149 to 171) for listing each plant in your garden, where you got it, when you planted it, and how it turned out.

☞ **Garden Plans** (pages 172 to 187) for designing new gardens or mapping existing ones.

☞ **Pests and Diseases** (pages 188 and 189) for noting which plants were attacked and which remedies were successful.

☞ **Addresses** (pages 190 to 192) for listing catalogs, nurseries, gardening services, and suppliers.

I think you will find this journal practical, logical, and easy to use. I hope it makes the time you spend in your garden more rewarding than ever.

Nancy K. Simpkins, October 1995
South Salem, New York

MONTHLY REMINDERS
Chores to complete this month:

JANUARY

FIRST WEEK DIARY

A year-to-year comparison

Year: _____

Year: _____

Weather notes:

Weather notes:

JANUARY

FIRST WEEK DIARY
A year-to-year comparison

Year: _____

Year: _____

Weather notes:

Weather notes:

J A N U A R Y

SECOND WEEK DIARY

A year-to-year comparison

Year: _____

Year: _____

Weather notes:

Weather notes:

JANUARY

SECOND WEEK DIARY
A year-to-year comparison

Year: _____

Year: _____

Weather notes:

Weather notes:

J A N U A R Y

THIRD WEEK DIARY
A year-to-year comparison

Year: _____

Year: _____

Weather notes:

Weather notes:

JANUARY

THIRD WEEK DIARY

A year-to-year comparison

Year: _____

Year: _____

Weather notes:

Weather notes:

FOURTH WEEK DIARY
A year-to-year comparison

Year: _____

Year: _____

Weather notes:

Weather notes:

FOURTH WEEK DIARY

A year-to-year comparison

Year: ———

Year: ———

Weather notes:

Weather notes:

JANUARY

PHOTOGRAPHS

Year: _____

Year: _____

PHOTOGRAPHS

Year: _____

Year: _____

JANUARY

MONTHLY REMINDERS
Chores to complete this month:

FIRST WEEK DIARY

A year-to-year comparison

Year: _____

Year: _____

Weather notes:

Weather notes:

FEBRUARY

FIRST WEEK DIARY
A year-to-year comparison

Year: _____

Year: _____

Weather notes:

Weather notes:

FEBRUARY

SECOND WEEK DIARY
A year-to-year comparison

Year: _____

Year: _____

FEBRUARY

Weather notes:

Weather notes:

SECOND WEEK DIARY
A year-to-year comparison

Year: _____

Year: _____

Weather notes:

Weather notes:

FEBRUARY

THIRD WEEK DIARY

A year-to-year comparison

Year: _____

Year: _____

Weather notes:

Weather notes:

FEBRUARY

THIRD WEEK DIARY

A year-to-year comparison

Year: _____

Year: _____

Weather notes:

Weather notes:

FOURTH WEEK DIARY
A year-to-year comparison

February

Year: _____

Year: _____

Weather notes:

Weather notes:

FOURTH WEEK DIARY
A year-to-year comparison

Year: _____

Year: _____

Weather notes:

Weather notes:

FEBRUARY

PHOTOGRAPHS

Year: _____

Year: _____

PHOTOGRAPHS

Year: _____

Year: _____

FEBRUARY

NOTES

FEBRUARY

MONTHLY REMINDERS
Chores to complete this month:

_____

_____

_____

_____

_____

_____

_____

_____

_____

_____

_____

MARCH

FIRST WEEK DIARY
A year-to-year comparison

MARCH

Year: _____

Year: _____

Weather notes:

Weather notes:

FIRST WEEK DIARY

A year-to-year comparison

Year: _____

Year: _____

Weather notes:

Weather notes:

MARCH

SECOND WEEK DIARY
A year-to-year comparison

Year: _____

Year: _____

MARCH

Weather notes:

Weather notes:

SECOND WEEK DIARY
A year-to-year comparison

Year: _____

Year: _____

Weather notes:

Weather notes:

MARCH

THIRD WEEK DIARY
A year-to-year comparison

MARCH

Year: _____

Year: _____

Weather notes:

Weather notes:

THIRD WEEK DIARY
A year-to-year comparison

Year: _____

Year: _____

Weather notes:

Weather notes:

MARCH

FOURTH WEEK DIARY

A year-to-year comparison

Year: _____

Year: _____

MARCH

Weather notes:

Weather notes:

Fourth Week Diary
A year-to-year comparison

Year: _____

Year: _____

Weather notes:

Weather notes:

MARCH

PHOTOGRAPHS

Year: _____

Year: _____

MARCH

Photographs

Year: _____

Year: _____

MARCH

MARCH

MONTHLY REMINDERS
Chores to complete this month:

_____
_____
_____
_____
_____
_____
_____
_____
_____
_____

FIRST WEEK DIARY

A year-to-year comparison

Year: _____

Year: _____

APRIL

Weather notes:

Weather notes:

FIRST WEEK DIARY
A year-to-year comparison

Year: _____

Year: _____

Weather notes:

Weather notes:

A P R I L

SECOND WEEK DIARY

A year-to-year comparison

Year: _____

Year: _____

Weather notes:

Weather notes:

SECOND WEEK DIARY
A year-to-year comparison

Year: _____

Year: _____

Weather notes:

Weather notes:

APRIL

THIRD WEEK DIARY
A year-to-year comparison

Year: _____

Year: _____

Weather notes:

Weather notes:

THIRD WEEK DIARY
A year-to-year comparison

Year: _____

Year: _____

Weather notes:

Weather notes:

APRIL

47

FOURTH WEEK DIARY

A year-to-year comparison

Year: _____

Year: _____

Weather notes:

Weather notes:

FOURTH WEEK DIARY

A year-to-year comparison

Year: _____

Year: _____

Weather notes:

Weather notes:

APRIL

PHOTOGRAPHS

Year: _____

Year: _____

PHOTOGRAPHS

Year: ———

Year: ———

APRIL

MONTHLY REMINDERS
Chores to complete this month:

FIRST WEEK DIARY
A year-to-year comparison

Year: _____

Year: _____

MAY

Weather notes:

Weather notes:

FIRST WEEK DIARY

A year-to-year comparison

Year: _____

Year: _____

Weather notes:

Weather notes:

SECOND WEEK DIARY
A year-to-year comparison

Year: _____

Year: _____

Weather notes:

Weather notes:

MAY

SECOND WEEK DIARY
A year-to-year comparison

Year: _____

Year: _____

Weather notes:

Weather notes:

MAY

THIRD WEEK DIARY
A year-to-year comparison

MAY

Year: _____

Year: _____

Weather notes:

Weather notes:

THIRD WEEK DIARY
A year-to-year comparison

Year: _____

Year: _____

Weather notes:

Weather notes:

M A Y

FOURTH WEEK DIARY

A year-to-year comparison

MAY

Year: _____

Year: _____

Weather notes:

Weather notes:

Fourth Week Diary

A year-to-year comparison

Year: _____

Year: _____

Weather notes:

Weather notes:

PHOTOGRAPHS

Year: _____

Year: _____

M A Y

Photographs

Year: _____

Year: _____

MAY

MONTHLY REMINDERS
Chores to complete this month:

J U N E

FIRST WEEK DIARY

A year-to-year comparison

Year: _____

Year: _____

Weather notes:

Weather notes:

JUNE

FIRST WEEK DIARY
A year-to-year comparison

Year: _____

Year: _____

Weather notes:

Weather notes:

J U N E

SECOND WEEK DIARY
A year-to-year comparison

Year: _____

Year: _____

Weather notes:

Weather notes:

JUNE

SECOND WEEK DIARY
A year-to-year comparison

Year: _____

Year: _____

Weather notes:

Weather notes:

J U N E

THIRD WEEK DIARY
A year-to-year comparison

Year: _____

Year: _____

Weather notes:

Weather notes:

JUNE

THIRD WEEK DIARY
A year-to-year comparison

Year: _____

Year: _____

Weather notes:

Weather notes:

J U N E

FOURTH WEEK DIARY
A year-to-year comparison

Year: _____

Year: _____

Weather notes:

Weather notes:

FOURTH WEEK DIARY
A year-to-year comparison

Year: _____

Year: _____

Weather notes:

Weather notes:

J U N E

PHOTOGRAPHS

Year: _____

Year: _____

Photographs

Year: _____

Year: _____

NOTES

MONTHLY REMINDERS
Chores to complete this month:

_____
_____
_____
_____
_____
_____
_____
_____
_____
_____
_____

First Week Diary

A year-to-year comparison

Year: _____

Year: _____

Weather notes:

Weather notes:

FIRST WEEK DIARY

A year-to-year comparison

Year: _____

Year: _____

Weather notes:

Weather notes:

79

SECOND WEEK DIARY
A year-to-year comparison

JULY

Year: _____

Year: _____

Weather notes:

Weather notes:

SECOND WEEK DIARY
A year-to-year comparison

Year: _____

Year: _____

Weather notes:

Weather notes:

J U L Y

THIRD WEEK DIARY
A year-to-year comparison

Year: _____

Year: _____

JULY

Weather notes:

Weather notes:

THIRD WEEK DIARY
A year-to-year comparison

Year: _____

Year: _____

Weather notes:

Weather notes:

J U L Y

FOURTH WEEK DIARY
A year-to-year comparison

Year: _____

Year: _____

Weather notes:

Weather notes:

JULY

FOURTH WEEK DIARY
A year-to-year comparison

Year: _____

Year: _____

Weather notes:

Weather notes:

PHOTOGRAPHS

Year: _____

Year: _____

JULY

Photographs

Year: _____

Year: _____

J U L Y

Monthly Reminders

Chores to complete this month:

FIRST WEEK DIARY
A year-to-year comparison

Year: _____

Year: _____

Weather notes:

Weather notes:

FIRST WEEK DIARY
A year-to-year comparison

Year: _____

Year: _____

Weather notes:

Weather notes:

91

SECOND WEEK DIARY

A year-to-year comparison

Year: _____

Year: _____

Weather notes:

Weather notes:

SECOND WEEK DIARY

A year-to-year comparison

Year: _____

Year: _____

Weather notes:

Weather notes:

A U G U S T

THIRD WEEK DIARY
A year-to-year comparison

AUGUST

Year: _____

Year: _____

Weather notes:

Weather notes:

THIRD WEEK DIARY
A year-to-year comparison

Year: _____

Year: _____

Weather notes:

Weather notes:

AUGUST

FOURTH WEEK DIARY
A year-to-year comparison

Year: _____

Year: _____

Weather notes:

Weather notes:

FOURTH WEEK DIARY
A year-to-year comparison

Year: _____

Year: _____

Weather notes:

Weather notes:

AUGUST

PHOTOGRAPHS

Year: _____

Year: _____

AUGUST

PHOTOGRAPHS

Year: _____

Year: _____

AUGUST

MONTHLY REMINDERS
Chores to complete this month:

SEPTEMBER

FIRST WEEK DIARY

A year-to-year comparison

Year: _____   Year: _____

Weather notes: Weather notes:

SEPTEMBER

FIRST WEEK DIARY

A year-to-year comparison

Year: _____

Year: _____

Weather notes:

Weather notes:

SEPTEMBER

SECOND WEEK DIARY

A year-to-year comparison

Year: _____

Year: _____

Weather notes:

Weather notes:

SECOND WEEK DIARY

A year-to-year comparison

Year: _____

Year: _____

Weather notes:

Weather notes:

SEPTEMBER

THIRD WEEK DIARY
A year-to-year comparison

SEPTEMBER

Year: _____

Year: _____

Weather notes:

Weather notes:

THIRD WEEK DIARY

A year-to-year comparison

Year: _____

Year: _____

Weather notes:

Weather notes:

FOURTH WEEK DIARY
A year-to-year comparison

Year: _____

Year: _____

Weather notes:

Weather notes:

Fourth Week Diary
A year-to-year comparison

Year: _____

Year: _____

Weather notes:

Weather notes:

S E P T E M B E R

PHOTOGRAPHS

Year: _____

Year: _____

PHOTOGRAPHS

Year: _____

Year: _____

NOTES

SEPTEMBER

MONTHLY REMINDERS
Chores to complete this month:

FIRST WEEK DIARY
A year-to-year comparison

Year: _____

Year: _____

Weather notes:

Weather notes:

FIRST WEEK DIARY
A year-to-year comparison

Year: _____

Year: _____

Weather notes:

Weather notes:

115

SECOND WEEK DIARY

A year-to-year comparison

Year: _____

Year: _____

Weather notes:

Weather notes:

SECOND WEEK DIARY
A year-to-year comparison

Year: _____

Year: _____

Weather notes:

Weather notes:

OCTOBER

OCTOBER

THIRD WEEK DIARY
A year-to-year comparison

Year: _____

Year: _____

Weather notes:

Weather notes:

THIRD WEEK DIARY
A year-to-year comparison

Year: _____

Year: _____

Weather notes:

Weather notes:

OCTOBER

FOURTH WEEK DIARY

A year-to-year comparison

OCTOBER

Year: _____

Year: _____

Weather notes:

Weather notes:

FOURTH WEEK DIARY

A year-to-year comparison

Year: _____

Year: _____

Weather notes:

Weather notes:

O C T O B E R

PHOTOGRAPHS

Year: _____

Year: _____

PHOTOGRAPHS

Year: _____

Year: _____

OCTOBER

OCTOBER

Monthly Reminders
Chores to complete this month:

N O V E M B E R

FIRST WEEK DIARY

A year-to-year comparison

NOVEMBER

Year: _____

Year: _____

Weather notes:

Weather notes:

FIRST WEEK DIARY

A year-to-year comparison

Year: _____

Year: _____

Weather notes:

Weather notes:

NOVEMBER

SECOND WEEK DIARY
A year-to-year comparison

NOVEMBER

Year: _____

Year: _____

Weather notes:

Weather notes:

SECOND WEEK DIARY
A year-to-year comparison

Year: _____

Year: _____

Weather notes:

Weather notes:

NOVEMBER

THIRD WEEK DIARY
A year-to-year comparison

NOVEMBER

Year: _____

Year: _____

Weather notes:

Weather notes:

THIRD WEEK DIARY
A year-to-year comparison

Year: _____

Year: _____

Weather notes:

Weather notes:

N
O
V
E
M
B
E
R

FOURTH WEEK DIARY

A year-to-year comparison

Year: _____

Year: _____

N O V E M B E R

Weather notes:

Weather notes:

FOURTH WEEK DIARY

A year-to-year comparison

Year: _____

Year: _____

Weather notes:

Weather notes:

NOVEMBER

PHOTOGRAPHS

Year: _____

Year: _____

PHOTOGRAPHS

Year: _____

Year: _____

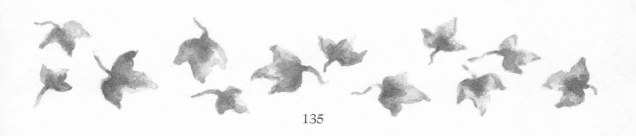

NOVEMBER

NOVEMBER

MONTHLY REMINDERS
Chores to complete this month:

FIRST WEEK DIARY

A year-to-year comparison

Year: _____

Year: _____

Weather notes:

Weather notes:

FIRST WEEK DIARY
A year-to-year comparison

Year: _____

Year: _____

Weather notes:

Weather notes:

139

SECOND WEEK DIARY

A year-to-year comparison

Year: _____

Year: _____

Weather notes:

Weather notes:

SECOND WEEK DIARY
A year-to-year comparison

Year: _____

Year: _____

Weather notes:

Weather notes:

D E C E M B E R

DECEMBER

THIRD WEEK DIARY
A year-to-year comparison

Year: _____

Year: _____

Weather notes:

Weather notes:

THIRD WEEK DIARY

A year-to-year comparison

Year: _____

Year: _____

Weather notes:

Weather notes:

143

DECEMBER

FOURTH WEEK DIARY
A year-to-year comparison

Year: _____

Year: _____

Weather notes:

Weather notes:

FOURTH WEEK DIARY

A year-to-year comparison

Year: _____

Year: _____

Weather notes:

Weather notes:

DECEMBER

PHOTOGRAPHS

Year: _____

Year: _____

DECEMBER

Photographs

Year: _____

Year: _____

DECEMBER

PLANT INVENTORY

Fill in the page headings and inventory plants by category (bulbs, roses, herbs, trees & shrubs), by garden (perennial border, shade garden, vegetable garden), or by location (greenhouse, window boxes, backyard border).

PLANT NAME	QTY.	WHERE PURCHASED	DATE PLANTED	COMMENTS

PLANT INVENTORY

PLANT NAME	QTY.	WHERE PURCHASED	DATE PLANTED	COMMENTS

PLANT NAME	QTY.	WHERE PURCHASED	DATE PLANTED	COMMENTS

PLANT INVENTORY

PLANT NAME	QTY.	WHERE PURCHASED	DATE PLANTED	COMMENTS

PLANT NAME	QTY.	WHERE PURCHASED	DATE PLANTED	COMMENTS

PLANT INVENTORY

PLANT INVENTORY

PLANT NAME	QTY.	WHERE PURCHASED	DATE PLANTED	COMMENTS

PLANT NAME	QTY.	WHERE PURCHASED	DATE PLANTED	COMMENTS

PLANT INVENTORY

PLANT NAME	QTY.	WHERE PURCHASED	DATE PLANTED	COMMENTS

PLANT NAME	QTY.	WHERE PURCHASED	DATE PLANTED	COMMENTS

P L A N T   I N V E N T O R Y

PLANT NAME	QTY.	WHERE PURCHASED	DATE PLANTED	COMMENTS

PLANT NAME	QTY.	WHERE PURCHASED	DATE PLANTED	COMMENTS

PLANT INVENTORY

PLANT NAME	QTY.	WHERE PURCHASED	DATE PLANTED	COMMENTS

PLANT NAME	QTY.	WHERE PURCHASED	DATE PLANTED	COMMENTS

PLANT INVENTORY

PLANT NAME	QTY.	WHERE PURCHASED	DATE PLANTED	COMMENTS

PLANT NAME	QTY.	WHERE PURCHASED	DATE PLANTED	COMMENTS

PLANT INVENTORY

PLANT INVENTORY

PLANT NAME	QTY.	WHERE PURCHASED	DATE PLANTED	COMMENTS

PLANT NAME	QTY.	WHERE PURCHASED	DATE PLANTED	COMMENTS

PLANT INVENTORY

PLANT INVENTORY

PLANT NAME	QTY.	WHERE PURCHASED	DATE PLANTED	COMMENTS

PLANT NAME	QTY.	WHERE PURCHASED	DATE PLANTED	COMMENTS

PLANT INVENTORY

	PLANT NAME	QTY.	WHERE PURCHASED	DATE PLANTED	COMMENTS

PLANT NAME	QTY.	WHERE PURCHASED	DATE PLANTED	COMMENTS

PLANT INVENTORY

	PLANT NAME	QTY.	WHERE PURCHASED	DATE PLANTED	COMMENTS

PLANT NAME	QTY.	WHERE PURCHASED	DATE PLANTED	COMMENTS

GARDEN PLANS

Use the graph paper to design a new garden or chart an existing one.
Number each plant. Then record its name on the following page.

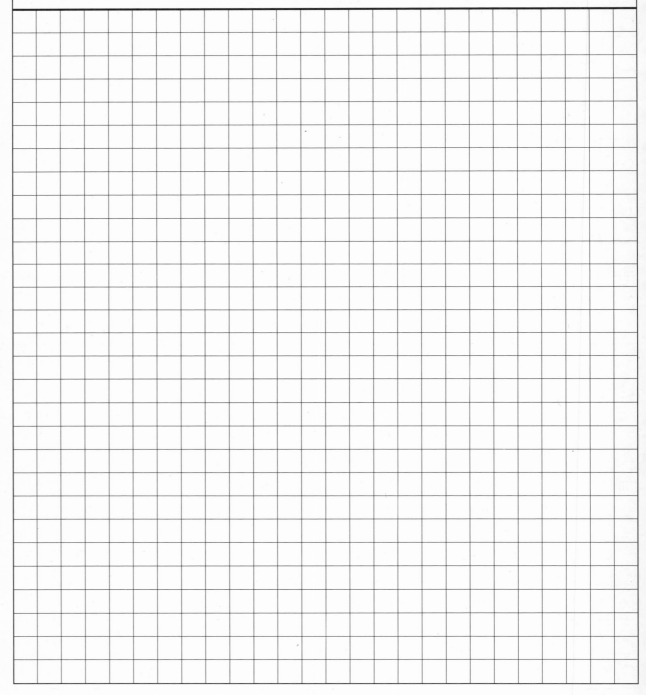

No.	Name	No.	Name

GARDEN PLANS

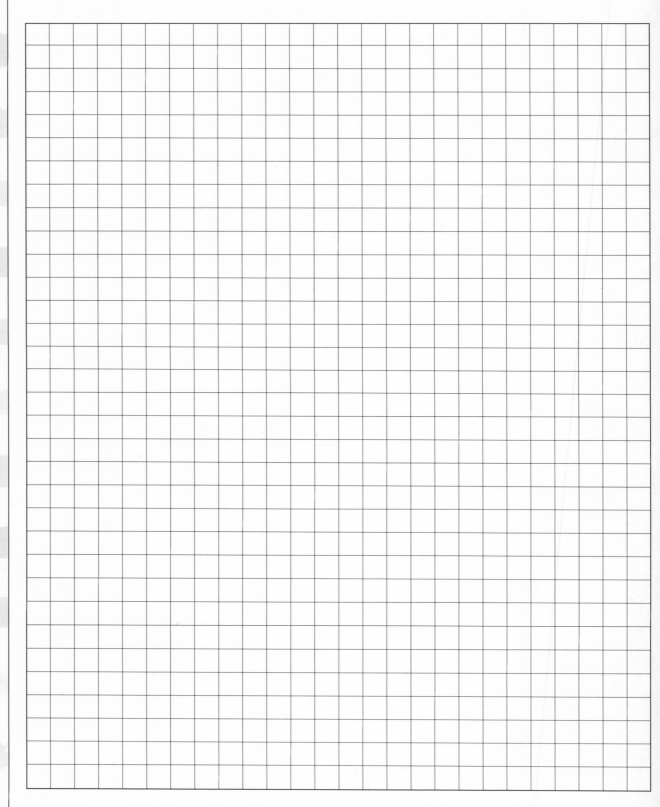

GARDEN PLANS

No.	Name	No.	Name

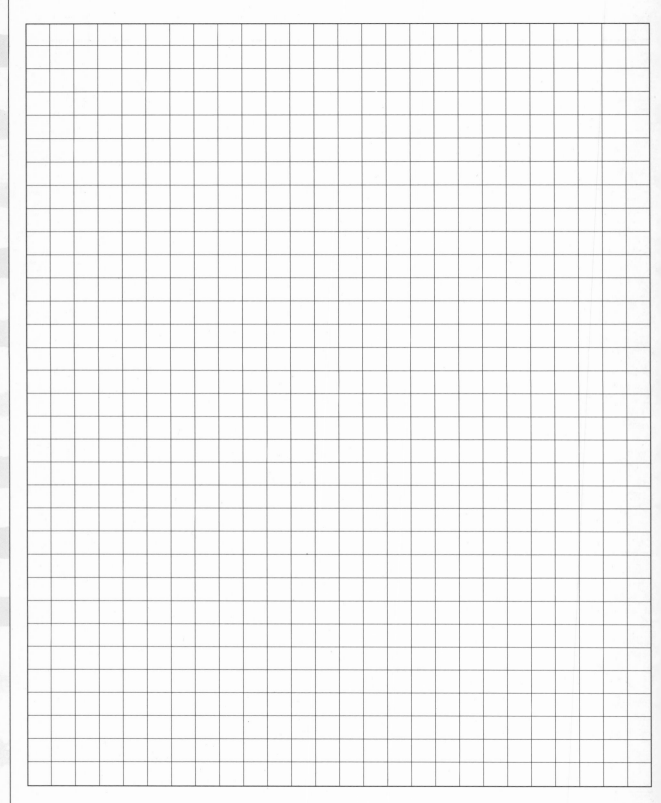

No.	Name	No.	Name

GARDEN PLANS

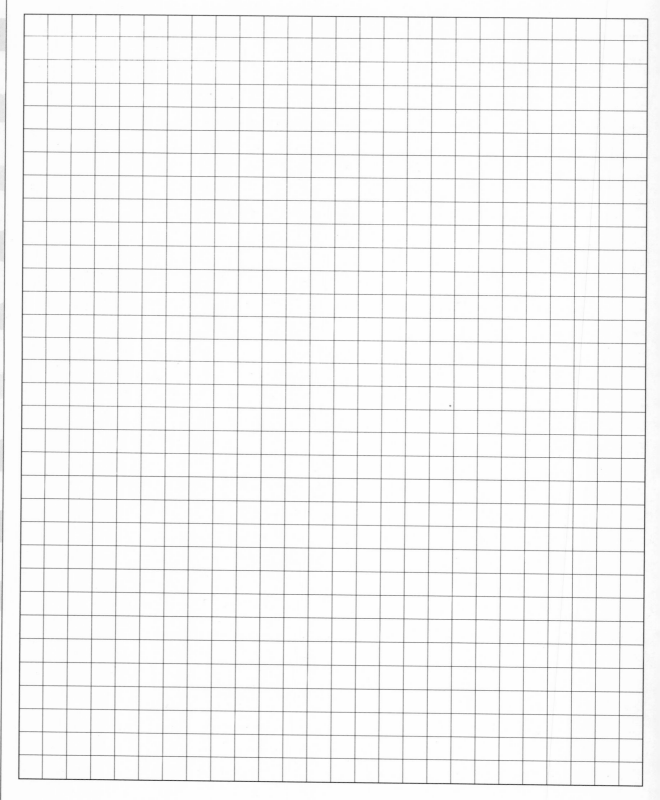

GARDEN PLANS

No.	Name	No.	Name

GARDEN PLANS

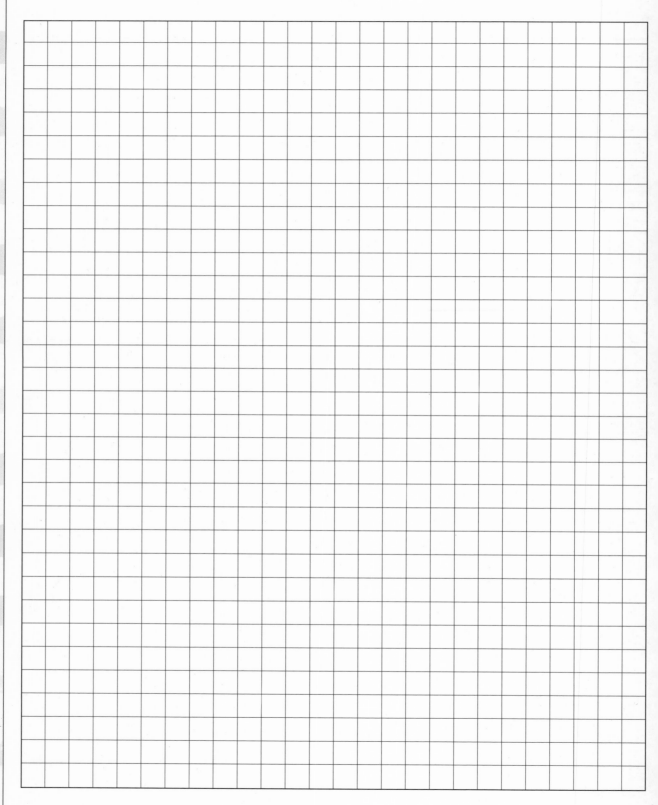

No.	Name	No.	Name

GARDEN PLANS

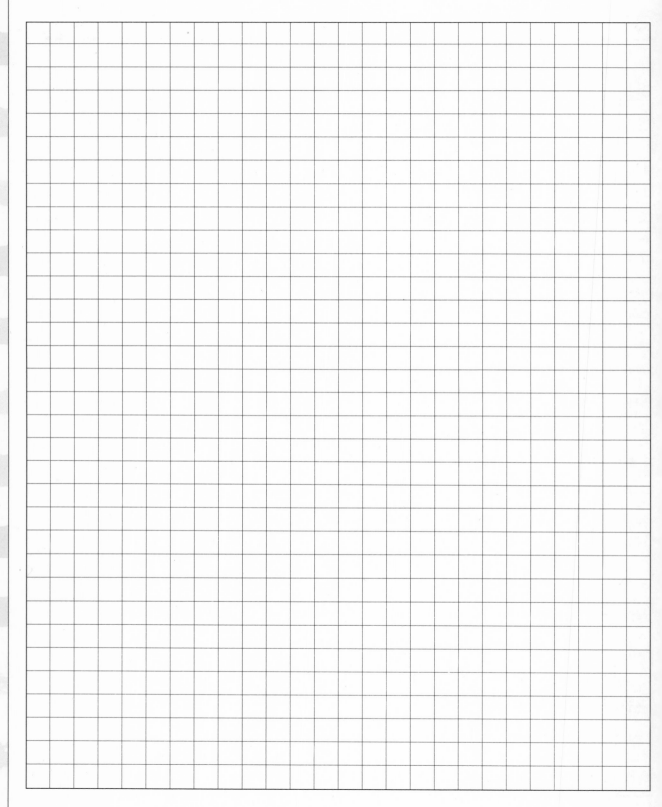

No.	Name	No.	Name

GARDEN PLANS

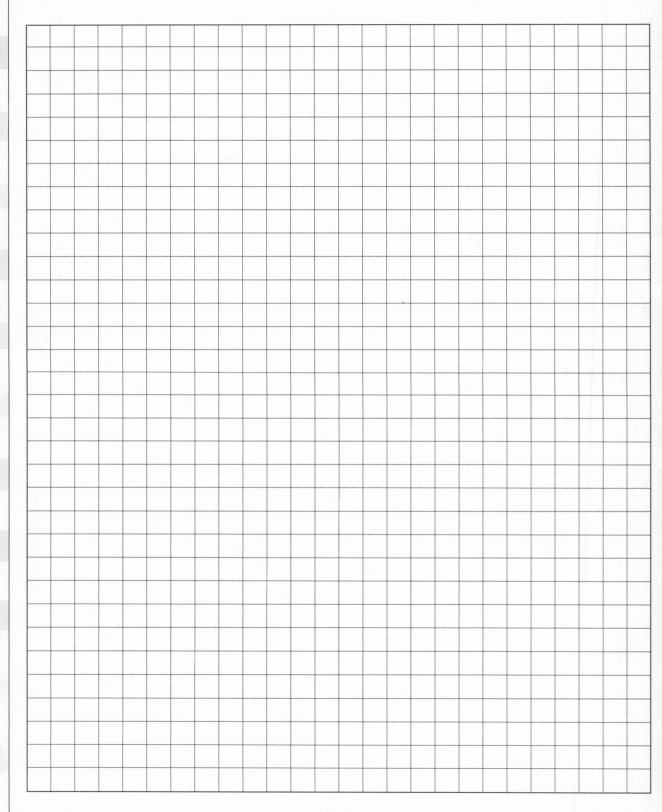

No.	Name	No.	Name

GARDEN PLANS

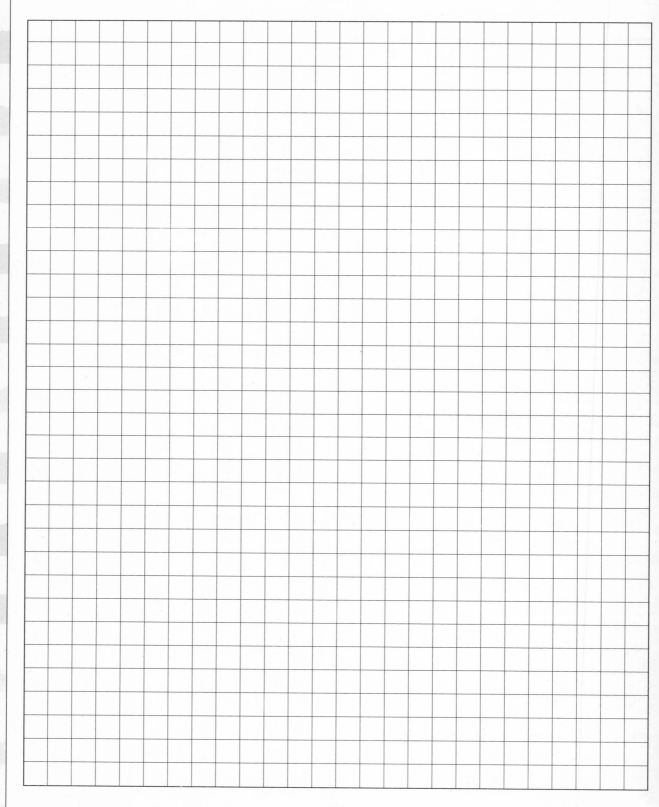

No.	Name	No.	Name

PESTS

PEST NAME	PLANTS UNDER ATTACK	SOLUTIONS

DISEASES

DISEASE NAME	PLANTS UNDER ATTACK	SOLUTIONS

ADDRESSES

Catalogs, nurseries, gardening services, and suppliers.

Name _____   Name _____

Address _____   Address _____

Phone _____   Phone _____

Specialties _____   Specialties _____

Name _____   Name _____

Address _____   Address _____

Phone _____   Phone _____

Specialties _____   Specialties _____

Name _____   Name _____

Address _____   Address _____

Phone _____   Phone _____

Specialties _____   Specialties _____

Name _____   Name _____

Address _____   Address _____

Phone _____   Phone _____

Specialties _____   Specialties _____

Name _____   Name _____

Address _____   Address _____

Phone _____   Phone _____

Specialties _____   Specialties _____

ADDRESSES

Name _____   Name _____

Address _____   Address _____

Phone _____   Phone _____

Specialties _____   Specialties _____

Name _____   Name _____

Address _____   Address _____

Phone _____   Phone _____

Specialties _____   Specialties _____

Name _____   Name _____

Address _____   Address _____

Phone _____   Phone _____

Specialties _____   Specialties _____

Name _____   Name _____

Address _____   Address _____

Phone _____   Phone _____

Specialties _____   Specialties _____

Name _____   Name _____

Address _____   Address _____

Phone _____   Phone _____

Specialties _____   Specialties _____

Name _____   Name _____

Address _____   Address _____

Phone _____   Phone _____

Specialties _____   Specialties _____

ADDRESSES

Name _____   Name _____

Address _____   Address _____

Phone _____   Phone _____

Specialties _____   Specialties _____

Name _____   Name _____

Address _____   Address _____

Phone _____   Phone _____

Specialties _____   Specialties _____

Name _____   Name _____

Address _____   Address _____

Phone _____   Phone _____

Specialties _____   Specialties _____

Name _____   Name _____

Address _____   Address _____

Phone _____   Phone _____

Specialties _____   Specialties _____

Name _____   Name _____

Address _____   Address _____

Phone _____   Phone _____

Specialties _____   Specialties _____

Name _____   Name _____

Address _____   Address _____

Phone _____   Phone _____

Specialties _____   Specialties _____